THE YOUNG SPORTSMAN'S GUIDE TO

GAME BIRDS

THE YOUNG SPORTSMAN'S LIBRARY

THE
YOUNG SPORTSMAN'S GUIDE
TO
GAME BIRDS

by

Ray Ovington

ILLUSTRATED BY FRANCIS W. DAVIS

THOMAS NELSON & SONS

Edinburgh   NEW YORK   *Toronto*

Acknowledgments

The author wishes to thank many people who have helped him through the years to know the creatures of the wilds. My father took me walking in the woods and when I grew up, put a gun and camera in my hands. His training was the beginning of an insight into the wild birds and animals, their habitat and their relationships with man.

Guides, outfitters, shooters, naturalists and authors of countless books helped in the early years of education.

I am also greatly indebted to Francis W. Davis, of Roscoe, N.Y., the illustrator of this book and its companion, *The Young Sportsman's Guide To Game Animals.*

Thanks too for the use in this book of certain material which has appeared in sportsman's magazines written over the years by the author.

Lowell Pratt and Angus Cameron have been of most inspiring help in my writing experience.

Lastly I appreciate the time made available to me to go afield by the New York *World-Telegram and Sun* while preparing my daily column "Hooks And Bullets."

© *1962, by Thomas Nelson & Sons*

All rights reserved under International and Pan-American Conventions. Published in New York by Thomas Nelson & Sons and simultaneously in Toronto, Canada, by Thomas Nelson & Sons (Canada), Limited.

Library of Congress Catalog Card No.: 62-12963

MANUFACTURED IN THE UNITED STATES OF AMERICA

Foreword

You are about to embark on an interesting study of a great collection of birds, the game birds. Much has been written about birds in general, but here you will find a specialized account of these particular species as they apply to the hunter, naturalist and photographer, where they are found, something about their habits and haunts.

This first bit of knowledge will be helpful to the first trips into the actual domain of these creatures and will to a large degree make your trips and hunts more enjoyable.

It is sincerely hoped that this guide will be read and reread and, perhaps, carried in your car or your jacket pocket while afield.

Merely to see a bird is not enough. To know something about it makes the sight more interesting. That is our purpose here.

Ray Ovington
Francis W. Davis

Contents

Acknowledgments 4

Foreword 5

CHAPTER I   *About Game Birds*   9

CHAPTER II   *Upland Game Birds*   12
Ruffed grouse   12
Prairie chicken   16
California valley quail   18
Gambel's quail   18
Bobwhite   21
Ringneck pheasant   23
Chukar   26
Hungarian partridge   26
Mourning dove   28
White-winged dove   28

CHAPTER III   *Lowland Game Birds*   30
Wild turkey   30
Jacksnipe   33
Woodcock   35
Clapper rail   38

CHAPTER IV   *Puddle Ducks*   40
Mallard   40
Black duck   44
European widgeon   47
Baldpate   47
American widgeon   47
Blue-winged teal   50
Green-winged teal   50
Cinnamon teal   50
Woodduck   53
Pintail   55
Gadwall   57

CHAPTER V   *Diving Ducks*   59
          Redhead   59
          Old squaw   61
          Ring-necked duck   63
          Greater scaup   66
          Lesser scaup   66
          Goldeneye   69
          Bafflehead duck   71
          Canvasback duck   73
          Shoveller duck   75
          "Coot"   76

CHAPTER VI   *Geese*   79
          Canada goose   79
          White-fronted goose   82
          American brant   84
          Black brant   84
          Blue goose   86

CHAPTER VII   *Game Birds, Your Heritage and*
          Responsibility   87

          Glossary   92
          Bibliography   93
          Index   94

Chapter I

About Game Birds

The study of American game birds will take you into all parts of the country and into all climates, seasons and kinds of wild land. You will visit the marshes, the fens and the lowland swamps and swales, the upland farms and fields, the broken woods patches and the high remote mountainous areas of our great land.

Various game birds are all over the map and are not difficult to identify, as are the many song birds such as the finches, warblers, sparrows and also birds of prey. A ruffed grouse, for instance, with his fan tail and peaked head supported by two black ruffs could not be mistaken in his environment for any other game bird. The ringneck pheasant could not be mistaken for a prairie chicken, even if it were seen on the prairie, nor could the Canada goose be mistaken for any other goose or duck.

There are, however, some difficult challenges for the bird watcher and hunter when it comes to many of the duck species, for they are most often seen under the difficult lights of dawn and dusk, and will often be in dark silhouette against the sun.

Many of the game species of land birds will be seen only in local conditions where they are generally found to feed, nest or migrate. For instance, it would be quite impossible for a ruffed grouse to be found in the Navajo country of Arizona, nor will you find the California Gambel's quail in the northernmost reaches of the state of Maine.

The study of these birds is a fascinating hobby, whether you are a photographer, bird watcher, hunting sportsman or all three. Knowing their habits around the calendar will in great

9

measure make it possible for you to "get their story" over the cyclic pattern of the year, for as the seasons change, so do their habits and habitats.

Many of the species in this book are migratory and therefore subject to protection by the federal government in cooperation with the southern states through which they pass in the fall and the northern states where they go to nest in the spring. In some areas they are seen only during the migration, despite the fact that some individuals see no reason for the trip and so stay the year round in comfortable surroundings, such as city parks, where they will be well fed and protected.

In order to study the species it is important to know what they look like. That is why I have collaborated with wildlife artist Francis W. Davis, who really knows these birds. You will also see his excellent artwork in the companion to this volume, *The Young Sportsman's Guide To Game Animals.*

Then comes the division of the species into categories for practical study and the accounting for those which are found to some extent either as residents or migrants in the area in which you live. However, it is well to know, at least theoretically, about the others, for you can never tell when a vacation trip or later travel in your lifetime will cause you to live or stay a while in the areas where other species reside.

Narrowing down the hunt for the game birds, we discover that the best times to study them are in the spring before much of the foliage is out and in the fall when the foliage is dropping from the brush and trees. At both these seasons game birds are the most active. Springtime is nesting time and being very shy, game birds will try to do their housework without detection, making the game of hide and seek a tough one for the person who does not know where or how to look for them. But since there is no hunting allowed in the spring, they are not quite so wary as they are in the fall months.

As the secrets of the species begin to unfold, the naturalist can go right to their nesting and feeding areas and quietly spy. Most game birds quietly sit out the summer after the little ones have left their nest and care, but in the fall, they are busy eating to prepare for the winter. Even the so-called residents do some migrating and moving about to the best feeding locations.

The bird watcher, photographer as well as hunter, can best find upland birds in the autumn with the use of a bird dog such as a pointer, setter, or spaniel. These dogs have the pointing instinct and flushing habit, so are traditionally used in locating, holding and flushing or "putting up" the birds for the hunter. Excellent photos can be taken during these hunts by the man who prefers to shoot with a camera.

Wildlife sanctuaries such as the Audubon sanctuaries, are wonderful spots for the study of the ducks and geese during the spring and fall migration seasons. It is possible there to identify and photograph as many as ten or fifteen species and to see clouds of migrating birds in the air at one time.

But before taking off with binoculars, gun or camera, the beginner can gain a great deal as a starter from the illustrations and information in this little volume. He can investigate further into the books listed in the bibliography. Then comes the visit to museums to see the mounted specimens. Quite often many zoos and game farms have these birds on exhibit. All this can be done even before the first walk into the woods and fields.

There is much material on hunting at the book stores and sporting goods stores giving tips and hints which can be used by nature lovers and photographers as well as hunters, for each is hunting, in that he wants to get a close look at the actual bird in its natural surroundings and to study its habits.

Much valuable information of this sort is available in the outdoor and nature magazines which print stories of hunts and stories about the various species. The Audubon Society publications, and the sporting magazines are most helpful. An example of the latter is *Sports Afield*. Quite often they feature very informative series on the game animals and birds of our country and ways to identify and find them.

Right now, let's study the headliners of the great outdoors.

Chapter II

Upland Game Birds

The most prized game bird of upland game hunters in the northern belt of states is the **ruffed grouse,** one of a large family of birds that inhabit North America. In the same family is the pinnated grouse commonly known as the prairie chicken. Other members of the family include the dusky grouse of the west, Franklin's grouse of the Pacific states, the Hudsonian grouse of northern Canada, sharp-tailed grouse of the western plains states and their numerous subspecies. In the Northeast they are found in company with the blue and spruce grouse. Ruffs weigh from one to two pounds average and are about sixteen inches in length.

The reason for singling out this particular one for study is the extreme esteem that hunters and naturalists hold for this most canny bird of the north woods. Books have been written about the craftiness of this bird and the ways and means of finding and outwitting him. The grouse vies for the honors with the Chinese pheasant as to which is the number one sport bird. To be sure there are more who hunt pheasants simply because they are more plentiful and easier to shoot, because they are largely farm birds. The grouse, on the other hand, is a creature of the wild forests and finds his home in deserted farms and open areas where the loggers have left brush growth in the forests.

The grouse is almost impossible to raise in captivity, so its restocking is much more difficult than with other birds. Mother Nature, then, is the grouse's only guide, with man its best friend and protector. Nature takes care of the grouse by constantly varying the cycle of abundance. When the birds become too crowded in a certain area, she steps in with a disease which

all but eliminates the species. Then, for a few years, the number of birds gradually increases again. Most conservation authorities have tried to follow these natural cycles in an effort to keep the birds at a more even level.

Grouse are readily identified by the black and brown-banded fan-shaped tail, the two tufts or ruffs on each side of the neck and the crested head. Both male and female are colored alike. There are two general hues of color, one gray and the other rust-red.

The most interesting time of the year is in the spring, when they are in the mating mood and when they can be seen and photographed while drumming on a log to attract a female. The whirr of their wings can be heard for some distance in the woods, as they vibrate their flight feathers in a terrific dance to impress their mate-to-be. At this time it is possible to approach with the camera for some excellent photos of the courtship.

The grouse's habitat is the deep woods rather than the open fields. They are sometimes quite tame in the wilderness, but are extremely wary when found in the vicinity of even sparse farm populations. Being a member of the chicken family, their habits are not unlike that of chickens. They roost on the ground or in trees and scratch for food, which is 90 per cent vegetable and 10 per cent insects. They often take dust baths along country roads, where they also eat gravel for their gizzards.

Unlike chickens, however, they do not travel in large flocks, preferring to be individuals. The hunter is lucky to flush more than two at a time in the deep woods. Four is the most I have ever seen in the air at one time. They were all young birds who had been raised together in one patch of woods.

Their flight when aroused is quick and erratic. They explode from the brush and quite often the gunner or observer is shocked momentarily because of the sudden sound coming from almost beneath his feet. The course of flight from there on out will be one of zig-zags through the leaves and branches as the bird tries to put as much natural cover between himself and you. No two grouse ever rise in the same way, so there is no characteristic flight to study in order to be a better shot. Hunters who are successful on grouse shoot instinctively. Somehow or other their shotgun barrels seem to point in the right direction, with enough lead to deliver the shot pattern on target. They are even harder to photograph because their course in the air is so unpredictable.

Grouse are best hunted with dogs, preferably a springer spaniel or perhaps an English setter. These dogs should be trained for grouse specifically, since grouse act entirely differently than pheasants or other game birds. A good quail dog is often at a loss, due to a strange and complicated terrain. The perfect experience is enjoyed with a good dog who is able to locate a grouse on the ground and hold it on point until the hunter moves up to flush it. If the bird is shot, its coloration blends so perfectly with the forest floor that the dog, with his keen sense of smell is relied upon to fetch it.

Grouse usually live to an age of about six years and are able to stand the severe winters of the northern climes. They are smart too, and in recent years boldly hold out in the face of real estate developments and advancing civilization. The key to their survival is food, mostly berries and seeds, and a good supply of unpolluted water. They prefer to live near the hemlock and pine forests where they can dodge their predators and take flight into the thick trees. Near their protective haunts, they must have a generous food supply year-round.

As the name implies, the **prairie chicken** is the bird with directly opposite haunts from the ruffled grouse. He is a bird of the Plains states and western provinces of Canada, with several close relatives in a smaller species known as the lesser prairie chicken, and also the sharp-tailed grouse and sage hen. The prairie chicken is also known as the pinnated grouse. Many of these birds once lived in the eastern states but because of wide cultivation of the fields and the leveling of the land, were gradually limited to the broader western lands. The heath hen is extinct because of man and, for that matter, several of the same general types are found now only in rare bands.

Fortunately the pinnated grouse has more territory at its beck and call and so was able to cope better than most of the others with the advances of civilization.

The prairie chicken is about the same size and shape as the ruffed grouse, but with more drab markings and a square tail, rather than a fan. Male chickens wear a slight crown on the head which is drab brown, unlike the darker crest of the ruffed grouse, and they sport two ruffs at the side of the neck which also do not contrast with the neck as much as the eastern partridge's ruffs contrast with his neck.

Chickens seem to successfully make the wide open spaces their home, and manage to hide well from predators and hunters, preferring to run away ahead of the gunners or dogs than risk flying into the air. When they do take wing, they do so with a frightening explosion and erratic air path. They are found more often in small flocks and so make relatively easy hunting. The urge to migrate is strong in the more northern climes. They prefer to miss the icy blasts and deep snow drifts and move south.

They mate in March and up until early May. A number of cock birds may gather at sunup to dance for their female prizes. They inflate yellow-colored air sacs on their neck until they resemble horns. They crackle and squawk as they reach the motions expel the air in booming sounds, which can be heard for some distance, to attract other hens to the scene. To further excite interest they raise the ruffs on the side of the necks to resemble horns. They crackle and squawk as they reach the climax of the mating dance.

This is quite an easy bird to photograph as he is so intent on the business at hand that one can approach quite closely. Females lay from eight to twelve eggs and the young leave the nest very soon after hatching to fend for themselves.

Both the **California valley quail** and the **Gambel's quail** and their many subspecies can be grouped together as they are all about the same size, of the same habits, with similar markings are found in the same general areas.

The Gambel's quail is about nine inches long and appears chestnut and purple-blue in color. The adult male is bluish-grey above with grey on his breast, but the belly is patched with buff and black. Head and throat are strikingly marked with bars of white and the rust-brown crown curves into a handsome black crest. The female is more drab in appearance. The California mountain quail is similar but with a more marked tassel on the top of the head.

These and their subspecies are birds of the semi-arid mountains and hill country of the Southwest and particularly California. They flock in coveys just like their cousins, the bobwhite and so offer great sport to bird hunters working their dogs, particularly the German short-haired pointer.

These quail seem to have taken to civilization very well and are found in and around the fringe of cities where there is water, food and cover. Quite often in the larger towns they will parade across people's lawns and live in the bushy undeveloped lots near homes, roads and factories. They do well in captivity and are raised for the table.

When they seek safety they tend to run at first rather than fly, streaking across the ground with head and neck out-stretched, their tassels bobbing as they go. When forced to take flight their air path is quite erratic, as with all the quail family. They do not fly too far generally, preferring to settle down in good cover until disturbed again. The hunter, knowing this can allow them to rest and regroup before coming upon them again for another try. Like all the quail family, they seem to believe in cooperative protection, often sleeping in a circular formation at night with all their heads pointed outwards from the circle.

They mate and breed in the spring and the female lays up to a dozen eggs, and sometimes has more than one clutch in a season.

They are subject to predators and sudden weather changes and in areas where they have been reduced by these conditions or by disease, the state conservation departments have protected them and restocked the broods with fresh blood from other areas. In general, they seem to be doing well despite the encroachments of civilization.

Their food varies according to range, the greatest part of it being seeds, buds and grains with berries as a second choice. Some insects are in the diet where the birds reside near watered areas. The hackberry bush is one of their mainstays, but they have been known to gorge themselves on bugs and particularly beetles and grasshoppers.

They spend most of the year in pairs or singles, gathering into varied flocks as high as sixty birds in the fall months. When spring comes they disband again just prior to finding their mate.

They do not have the familiar "bobwhite" call such as their eastern cousin, but make up for this in the plumage beauty.

The **bobwhite** is truly America's favorite, a true native of this country, with its whistle call that has made it one of the most famous birds of the world. The "bobwhite" bell-like notes immediately help to locate the bird in the cover and a cheery sound it is to the bird watcher, the wildlife photographer and the hunter.

It is a brave little bird and a "smart alec" of the fields and farmlands, preferring to live near the farmer rather than be a recluse in the forest.

"Bob" at one time lived over most of the land, with several subspecies still prevailing to this day in almost all but the most frigid parts of the country. His stronghold is in the states south of New York, Michigan and Oregon, liking the vacation land of Florida, Georgia, Virginia, the south central Mississippi Valley and the Southwest, where he is found in great abundance. The plantation owners of the South have kept their covers well-birded by introducing wild strains with pen-raised stock to keep the coveys large and strong for hunters.

At one time, "Mr. White" lived well in New England, but during the past twenty years has steadily decreased in number.

In New Jersey though he still thrives despite the winters, land reclamation and development. Before rifles were made unlawful in the counties near New York City, sportsmen shot off the predators and the quail thrived. Few are found now in Westchester and nearby counties, unless stocked on private preserves.

This quail is a checkerboard of browns, tans, yellows and off-white with black streaks here and there to further help in his camouflage. He is a very small bird, weighing a scant half to three-quarter pounds, is short-tailed, fast and erratic in flight. Enough of his numbers in the frying pan can make quite a dinner.

Bobwhites prefer to stick together in coveys, roosting and feeding together and rising in a group when put up by dogs. They are easy to photograph and, as mentioned, simple to locate by their famous whistle call that can usually be heard across the fields from dawn to dusk.

Famous sportsmen and farm hands alike love him for the continued sport he offers. His one weak point is low resistance to bad weather and disease, but conservation methods have been developed to keep his numbers high enough so we will always hear his call.

Though not a native American bird, the **ringneck** or **China pheasant** is an import from the Far East. He's done much better in the face of stiff competition with predators and the advance of civilization than any of the other imports and will also probably survive much longer than any of our native game species. He has to contend with hunters, real estate developers, dogs, housecats, game poachers and attacks of disease, droughts, fires and floods, but does well in spite of them all.

He is the easiest of all game birds to recognize, since there is no other upland game bird with a bright green head and neck supported by a white ring at its base. His barred, unusually long and broad tail is his second fast identifying feature. He's a big bird, weighing from two to three pounds, which is larger than a grouse and about half as big as the usual wild turkey.

Ringneck is the most popular hunting bird of all found in natural "native" stock throughout the northern states and as far south as Florida. He has traveled west to California, Oregon and Washington, either by natural breeding or by conservation truck. Where he is shot out or dies out from disease or other causes, he is easily restocked by private or other governmental agencies.

Commercial shooting preserves stock this bird in their covers where shooting is heavy and constant during the fall and winter months. In areas close to the big cities, where shooting pressure is too great in open lands, the shooting preserve and the ringneck is the only answer to shooting sport.

"Chink" is a grand bird, rising in a flurry of feathers, cackles and wingbeats dragging his magnificent tail and often waving it in a hunter's face. Best hunting is with a bird dog from the little cocker spaniel to the bigger pointers and setters. The birds are usually quite gregarious, and it is often possible to flush as many as ten at a time. Best territory for their natural growth is in the corn and wheat-belt states of the midwest. They do well also in areas where the foliage is fairly broken between forest and farmland and where there are fields broken by strips of trees and brush.

This bird is a hybrid of many species, but now has become a distinct species here in America. It is a cross between the English pheasant and the Mongolian pheasant, all quite similar in appearance. Since the strains have been intermingled over a period of time, they have developed into a strong bird which resists disease and has become smart in the face of encroaching civilization. They are often found nesting in the broken country-like patches of fields between private homes and often seen flying across main traffic arteries such as the modern parkways.

When hunted over to any extent the wild birds become very smart and crafty. They will run well ahead of even the best of bird dogs and escape. They will also fly low when flushed, keeping the dog in the line of the gun, thus causing the shooter to withhold his fire from fear of killing or wounding the animal.

Pheasant are easily pen-raised even by amateurs and many farmers raise them for the market and the table. 4H Clubs across the nation have a pheasant-raising course and contests to develop interest in aiding the conservation departments. Many states encourage 4H-clubbers by offering to pay them for raising the birds from the eggs to maturity and to help stock them in local cover.

Judged the most beautiful of all the hunting fowl, the pheasant is a godsend to our country. The male averages about two and three-quarter pounds and specimens in good wild cover usually weigh a bit more.

One of the easiest birds to locate and identify, they offer the best opportunity for the beginner at spotting, photography and hunting. They are also very good for training the young hunting dog.

The **chukar,** an import from India, Asia and Africa, and the **Hungarian partridge** from Europe can be grouped together for this study. Their markings and habits are somewhat similar and they are found generally in the northern prairie states and into Canada, having gained a foothold there after repeated failures in other parts of the Northern Hemisphere. They are also found as artificial plantings on the many commercial shooting preserves particularly in the East and in California.

The chukar is a fast flying bird that quickly understands what the hunter is up to when shot over to any degree and so offers exciting work with gun and dog. It is a short-tailed partridge of soft grey coloration marked with greyish-brown bars on the flanks. The feet and the bill are coral-red. It weighs a little more than the "Hun," from one to one and one-half pounds, while the "Hun" rarely weighs over a pound. The "Hun" is more plump in shape, greyish over-all but with defined chestnut-colored bar markings on the flanks. Both are seed and grain eaters and seem to survive well on farms of the Middle West and lately in the more southern states.

Sportsmen looked to these imports to bolster the failing crop of quail, and pheasant in certain areas. They have not been disappointed in the sporting qualities of the species, but have had a hard time in establishing them so that they will breed in the wild where they are most needed.

Chukars and "Huns" are a covey-type bird and in habits not unlike the native quail. They hold well to a good dog and when they take wing their flight is speedy and direct, similar to our bobwhite.

While both species are strong birds, they have yet to reach the status of the pheasant even in their most established range. It is hoped, however, that through the years, the future generation of these birds will build up to the rigors of life in America and that both will become well established "natives."

They are a good bird as a table delicacy, and also make good decorations for the den as mounted specimens, being a trifle more colorful than the American quail.

Their breeding and nesting times are similar to all quail and their habit of gregariousness makes them a good bird to hunt as they will generally rise in groups rather than in singles or pairs.

Hunters refer to the **mourning dove** and the **white-winged dove** as **"the pigeon"** in their hunting. The white-wing is a western variety and the mourning dove is a species found all over the entire country from southern Canada to Mexico. While classed as a migratory bird, they usually stay the winter when the weather allows.

They are both related to the passenger pigeon which is now long extinct due to overshooting and market-hunting, plus disease, which plagued the huge flocks that covered the land a hundred years ago.

The mourning dove is recognizable by its long triangular tail and its white border. The wings, like those of all doves, are long, slim and pointed, giving them a swift and erratic flight that appeals to gunners who try to sight it correctly in pass shooting when the doves are returning to their feeding or roosting locations.

They are ground feeders and their chief staple of diet is grains. They can be seen quite often along highways taking dust baths and eating gravel for their digestion. They generally nest in trees, the nest being made of small twigs. Two or more eggs are laid and sometimes they lay as many as three clutches a year.

Their mournful cry or coo is a sure way of locating them for identification and pictures. They are exceedingly tame and will come in to the feeding station in your yard.

The whitewing dove is a hunters' favorite particularly in California and other western states. Its habits are somewhat similar to the mourning dove except that it can live in much drier climate. Patches of white on the wing are the main identification marks. The two species are distinct and could never be confused.

They are fun to hunt, and the only time that they can be taken is during their flights from roost to feeding locations and back. While on the wing from these two locations they fly fast and usually in a direct course, appearing out of nowhere, dashing between the trees or suddenly veering off at the sight, sound or feeling of danger.

They are an excellent table bird, though small in size.

The number of wild pigeons is holding up well and they are in little danger of extinction, particularly the mourning variety.

Chapter III

Lowland Game Birds

The familiar barnyard gobbler is the same species as the **wild turkey.** It has merely adapted itself, with the aid of man, to live with the other fowl of the farm rather than stay in woods where it first came from.

Everybody knows what the barnyard turkey looks like, since he is the traditional bird of the Thanksgiving and Christmas table. The early explorers of our country depended upon him for many a main course at the family table.

Yet, this bird in the wild state is perhaps the most tricky and hardest to stalk of any of the game birds of America (due to its shy and alert nature) even though it is a large bird, our largest. He is a recluse of the dense forests, hardly ever ranging in the open country particularly when men with guns are abroad. In the early days the wild turkey roamed over almost all the land, but the inroads of civilization caused him to retreat until today he is found only in the remotest woods and swamps. Conservation departments of the various states where where he formerly lived in peace are trying to stage a comeback for him by restocking and protecting him from over hunting and predators. It is a long hard pull against heavy odds. In New York State, for instance, stocking the woods of the state forests has gradually re-established the bird in several very small areas. Working from farmer stock bred with captured wild birds, a strain has been developed which seems to be holding on. The southland states of Florida, Georgia and their neighbors have many areas where the wild turkey is still found in great abundance.

This is the only game bird which can also be shot legally with a rifle as well as a shotgun. Dogs are no help in turkey hunting. The hunter uses a small call to attract the bird, or attempts to hold his attention until he can be seen or approached. The turkey will run every time rather than flush into the air. It is a rare and beautiful sight to see one streaking through the pines in full flight with its powerful wings biting the air and its magnificent tail spread.

The male grows to a length of forty-eight inches, the female, usually about thirty-seven inches. Both have a wing-spread of about five feet, and weigh between fifteen and twenty pounds.

Gobblers live where they can feed on acorns, nuts, berries, plants, seeds, and insects. They lay between nine and eighteen eggs, each spring and grow to a ripe old age of twelve years.

Their tail feathers were used by the Indians for tribal costumes, especially when eagle feathers were not obtainable. Today their feathers are of value to trout fly tiers and are also for other decorative purposes. As for their use as food, they are much superior in flavor to their farm-raised brothers, but of course, the flabby farm stock is much more tender.

If you live in an area where the turkey was once a "native," try to get the local gun club boys to cooperate with the state conservation department to attempt reintroducing the turkey to your woodlands. You can probably enlist the help of an owner of private posted land, or use an Audubon sanctuary for your initial stocking.

The **Jacksnipe,** or **common snipe,** is found 'round the world wherever there is dampness, mud and worms, and has entertained hunters and naturalists for many years.

It is a native bird which migrates south only when forced to by bad winter weather. It is very similar to many of the other snipe and shore birds and the hunter has to be very careful not to shoot birds that are protected. Because it is a migrator, it is itself protected by federal regulations modified by the various states in which the bird resides or travels. Many states do not have an open season on the bird.

For many years the jack, along with other shore birds was heading for a low point, and possible extinction. Much market hunting combined with extensive swamp drainage helped in large measure, to cause their downfall. In recent years they have been making a slow comeback until it has been possible to open the season on them in some states.

They are readily identified by their long bill, striped head and, when walking or standing, their long neck. Their habit of constantly tipping up in a nervous jerk is common to all the snipe tribe. Their movement on their long thin legs is fast and constant as they look for food along the banks, near the water and in the grassy muddy spots along lake shores, inlets and swamps.

Snipe are active mostly at dusk and dawn, flocking at these times to some extent. During the day they are relatively inactive and not too easy to locate.

When surprised they utter a rasping "escape, escape" blurping sound and usually utter it as they take off from the ground. Usually they are found by hunters in small bands, but take to the air, one or two at a time. They can be approached quite easily in the high grass. They will make short flights ahead of the gunners to be easily put up again. About the third or fourth time they will rise too far ahead of the shooters.

They can be attracted by decoys made to their shape and size. Usually these are placed along a shoreline known to be visited by them at feeding times. When the flight passes over and sees the decoys they generally light among them, look them over and start feeding, forgetting that they are there. This is the time for the photographer who is armed with a flash gun to get his pictures.

The **woodcock** is called the **"Timberdoodle"** by hunters and bird watchers, and is one of the trickiest fliers of all the game birds and the most difficult to locate in singles or in flocks. They are migratory and are seen best during the spring and fall periods of movement since they flock up at these times. "Woodies" are small, seldom weighing over a quarter of a pound.

Woodcock differ from other similar shore and marsh birds in that they have a very short neck, supporting a small head and extra long bill. In flight their head seems to be set right on their shoulders just ahead of their fast beating wings. They have very big eyes and their upper parts are colored like a confusion of dead leaves. Only their head has conspicuous bar markings of alternating black and light tan.

Woodcock are solitaries, preferring the swamps, wet woods and damp thickets. They feed mostly at dawn, dusk and through the night and can be found wherever there are muddy sections where they can find succulent worms and grubs.

During the migrating season, particularly in the northeastern states, the birds from as far north as Newfoundland and Nova Scotia mix with the resident birds to form an enlarged population for the bird watcher and hunter. The first cold rains and winds of fall generally start them on their southern trip and it is at this time that hunters seek them out for what is known as the greatest little game bird in all the land.

When they rise either in front of a lone hunter or a sporting dog, they do not run or hide as the pheasant or turkey, but rise boldly into quick dashing flight straight up and out. Usually they sound off with a surprised burplike call. Even though they travel in flocks they seldom rise together. More than three or four rising at once would be the exception.

The female lays from two to five eggs and the young quickly learn the ways to the nearest mud puddle and start digging with their bills for worms and grubs.

Since they are migratory, they are subject to federal as well as state government conservation laws and, as such, will be protected from overshooting and guaranteed protection along their migratory routes with wildlife sanctuaries. Much of their natural breeding grounds and feeding stations have been developed for real estate and farming, but their protection is assured for years to come.

This game bird is a "cycle" bird, vulnerable to periodic disease and thus great variances in numbers. One year, the flight will be exceptionally large and then the next year there will be only a few birds. They are not strong and therefore cannot resist sudden and drastic temperature changes. Since their food consists mostly of worms if they fail to depart for the South soon enough, whole flocks can suddenly perish. They are also subject to pollution, and since many of our mud flat areas are often polluted, this is a source of trouble.

I have done some of my best woodcock hunting in Nova Scotia, Maine and central New York State, and often found them in company with the ruffed grouse, though generally they prefer the more swampy areas and damp thickets.

Photographing the woodcock on the ground is quite an experience. It calls for exceptional ability to stalk. A good bird dog that will "hold" the bird to the ground for long periods of time before flushing is almost a requisite, unless you are filming the nest in the springtime. Catching them in the air on film is another difficult trick, but can be done if you consider your camera as a gun and actually "shoot" the bird in flight. You will seldom get a second chance. If you do manage to get a good unblurred photo of a woodcock in the air you can be most proud.

The best hours are morning and evening. This calls for a flash gun attachment on your camera and a mighty bright one.

Like the feathers of many of the birds described in this book, those of the woodcock are extremely valuable for fly-tying purposes. If you happen to be a trout fisherman, or have a fisherman friend, always save the wings on game birds, and the flank feathers as well on all ducks.

F.W.Davis

"Let's go rail hunting!" is the suggestion which is made each September by hunters along the Eastern Seaboard from Maine to Florida. Despite the fact that there are several species of gallinules (rails) quite similar to each other, the **clapper rail** is the game species. It is important to know how to distinguish this bird from the others, for shooting the wrong one will mean breaking the law.

"Mr. Clapper" is a sixteen inch long bird with a rather long bill, heavy though rather long neck supported by a rather plump body, and broad wings which in turn is supported by long legs and feet equipped to carry it with speed across the mud flats and marshes.

The forehead is a dusky color, the rest of the body a pale olive, ashy color. The distinct identifying marks are on the underparts and under the tail, colored with alternating bands of off-white and muddy rust.

Hunting technique is employed usually by the use of a boat or scow which is paddled and poled along the edges of marshes and swamps, or along the streams coursing through the muck. Some hunters walk and wade, but in most cases this proves to be a hard job with the possibility of a dangerous fall or a sinking into the mire. The birds are generally easy to locate and will flush quite near the gun at the beginning of the season. After they have been hunted over for some time, they become smart and run for quite a distance before taking off. They are not a covey bird so seldom rise up in a group. Usually they flush in singles or at the most, in pairs.

Why rail hunting has become popular is a mystery to some sportsmen. Certainly the bird is no great taste treat at the table, nor is it a particularly tricky flier. Perhaps it is because this is the first bird that is legal at the beginning of the hunting season that brings the sportsmen out.

Their nests make interesting subjects for the wildlife photographer. They are easily discovered and the parents don't seem to mind too close intrusion. The little ones, numbering usually from six to fifteen are glossy black in color, and are quite clumsy, waddling and swaying in their nest of dead grasses set on a platform in a clump of high grass. They seem to like to nest in communities. Where you find one nest you will usually find several nearby. While out visiting them you will also become acquainted with several other rail and shorebird species of interest, although they are, except for the jacksnipe, protected from gunning.

Chapter IV

Puddle Ducks

Due to its broad distribution along boat coasts and through-out the inland lakes and marshes, the **mallard** or **"greenhead"** is the most sought after of our waterfowl. It is the prettiest in the minds of some, since it has been the most common subject of painters and wildlife artists. Mallard decorations and mini-ature decoys grace many a sportsman's library or den. Only the shoveller and the woodduck vie for or possibly surpass his beauty. The drake has a blue-green iridescent head and neck, ringed at the base by a narrow white band. The blue-purple patch banded with white on the first section of the wing and his yellow legs mark him unmistakably. Many hunters call him "yellowlegs." The female is speckled with various shades of brown, but she also wears the blue-purple patches on the wings.

The mallard offers one of the best opportunities to break in on the study of waterfowl. You find them in most city parks the year round. You'll also find the domesticated variety on the farm. Commercial shooting preserves stock him for this type of pass shooting.

Many of the species do not migrate, preferring to stay in one place unless molested by predators, pollution, over-hunting or extremely bad weather. Since all ducks are migratory, numbers of mallards in company with black duck, widgeon, teal, pintail, and others, take off for the south for the winter and travel as far as Central America. In the spring they go as far north as Alaska and Newfoundland, following established migrating routes. These routes have been discovered by the extensive method of leg banding, a research that has been going on now for about fifty years.

The mallard, like all puddle ducks, rises quickly from the water in one frantic bound. It does not need to take off on a long runway of water as do its cousins, the diving ducks. While it rises off the water with a terrific flourish, it does not seem to be a fast flier in comparison with the teal, but does offer quite a sight to the naturalist or camera man and much more so to the gunner who tries to lead it correctly with the shotgun.

Mallards decoy readily to artificial replicas set out in the corner of a pond or near the rushes where they would come in to feed at dusk or dawn. One of the best ways to study these birds is to decoy them in this manner, having built a blind of natural grasses. Get to know a duck hunter and accompany him on his trip to the duck blind. Bring your camera along to record the birds as they bounce from the air, light on the water, or, sensing danger quickly change pace and direction to fly away almost before you have had the time to take your pictures.

Greenheads will often circle high overhead, spot the decoys and then come sailing in on set wings to alight among the "blocks," as the hunters call their decoys.

Pass shooting, that is, lying in wait for the birds to pass a given location, is another way of shooting them with camera or gun. When their route is known from their lake site to their feeding site, the area in between makes a good position to wait for them to pass overhead.

Jump shooting can also be done by silently gliding in a canoe or row boat down a winding river where the ducks are known to live and feed. Coming upon them suddenly will offer ample opportunities to see them in action.

Mallards vary in weight from a pound to three or four pounds depending on the condition and location and are among the best of ducks as a table staple. As none of the puddle ducks eat fish, they do not have a fishy taste. Their diet is mostly roots and shoots of aquatic plants, grain, nuts and seeds. The mallard feeds by ducking his head underwater to grope for these aquatic plants and shoots of grass. On land, "Mr. Mallard" is fond of grains, particularly corn and rice.

You should be able to get some fine shots of the courting which takes place in the spring of the year, and certainly a photo of the drake and hen with their little ducklings should grace any sportsman's den or photographer's studio.

Despite the inroads of civilization on their breeding grounds, the migrating areas and general development of watercourses, the mallard and his next of kin, the black duck, seem to be able to cope with worsening conditions.

Being versatile and adaptable, the federal government and state conservation departments have concentrated on protecting him and his grounds and restocking him, all with good results.

Like all migratory waterfowl, the mallard is protected by federal gunning seasons which are followed by state enforcement with acceptable dates. The photographer, however, can "shoot" the mallard and other easily found ducks the year 'round.

Greenheads nest in parks, along brooks and in swamps, anywhere near the water and food supply. Normally one clutch of eggs is laid each season, ranging from six to ten, but sometimes they will raise two or more broods if conditions warrant.

Young sportsmen who are interested in the art of taxidermy, that is the artistic mounting or "stuffing" of birds, can practice on the mallard, for he is the most available in many areas of the country. The practice mounts can be used later as decoys. Any den is made more beautiful by the addition of a brace mounted in flying position over the fireplace or against the wall.

Photographing the mallard, or any wildfowl, requires the best camera you can afford. Have one you can quickly recock and rewind in order to get in a second shot. Shoot at as fast a speed as light will allow, or arrange to take the photos at double or triple the film rating and have them developed to this prescription.

Mallards can easily be baited by planting rice or other aquatic foods of their liking around the pond or lake nearest you. Many gun clubs and sanctuaries do this. The actual practice of baiting, that is placing corn or grain in plain sight during the hunting season is against the law. However, it is allowable if you do not intend to shoot the birds. Just make sure you remove the grains before leaving the area.

The **black duck** is primarily an eastern species, ranging from Labrador and Newfoundland to Pennsylvania and North Carolina in the breeding and summer months, to the southern states, Mexico and Central America in the winter. Theirs is a very interesting pattern of migration and flock concentrations as shown by annual charts made up of recovered legbands from birds either found dead or shot by hunters. Banding is an important phase of duck and duck habitat research and sportsmen are urged to return tags immediately with the needed information to whatever address is on the tag.

There are two species of black ducks and the scientists are still arguing the points of distinction. One is smaller than the other, but from that point on, there is not much of a noticeable difference. As birds of one species can vary as much as a pound or more, telling the difference is quite a proposition.

The black duck is not really black. The male and female are colored about the same; with light tan heads and necks speckled with darker brown-tipped feathers. The body colors are rich brown with a darker, almost purplish cast, and their breasts are slightly lighter in color. The wings support the blue-purple patch similar to the mallard in both male and female.

Their legs are a brilliant reddish-orange and so they are nicknamed "redlegs."

This species is quite similar to the mallard in breeding season, locations, feeding habits and migration along the coast. They are often found in company with them and the other pond or puddle ducks, particularly the gadwall, pintail and widgeon.

Blacks decoy readily and are easily lured to the gunner's blind as are the mallards by the proper use of a duck call, imitating their calling and talking sounds to bring them in to properly placed decoys of either mallard or black duck colors. They are quite often more wary than the mallard and are generally more adaptable to East Coast conditions. There are more blacks on the Eastern Seaboard than almost any other species, and most of them stay the year round unless the ice and snow force them into going farther south.

While not as pretty a bird as the mallard, their habits are well worth knowing because of their large supply and they offer a greater opportunity for watching throughout the year than almost any other species.

"Redlegs" generally weigh a bit more than most mallards and are considered as good as the mallard on the dinner table. Their natural food is the same as the mallard, although they tend to stick more closely to the natural foods rather than resort to corn and other field grains.

Along our two coasts, they tend to feed and breed in the salt marshes and inland waterways where brackish water is present. At times this is reflected in their taste, but it is never fishy as the diving ducks at their very best.

Since they breed over a wide range, it behooves the sportsman to try and provide areas where they can nest and feed in peace. Many thousands reside in the sanctuaries and parks. Much work is needed to increase as well as maintain the present wetlands where all ducks feed and breed. The young sportsman can do the most good by joining a rod and gun club and working on such projects locally.

The black is the traditional duck of the hunter. A fascinating side study would encompass the history of duck shooting in America from the days of the market hunters to the present day.

The gradual improvement of duck blinds and decoys is part of that history. Some decoys located in old homes or boat houses have become quite valuable as collector's items. Browse around old book stores and perhaps you will find old hunting prints of duck shooting. They make a substantial addition to your den or study.

The **European widgeon,** a popular game bird of eastern Europe, is closely related to our **baldpate** or **American widgeon,** and is a common visitor to the Eastern Seaboard of America. It is also found occasionally on the West Coast. Since they are so similar in basic markings, they are considered here together. The difference in identification can be found in the variance of the underwing surface color. If it is whitish and mottled with dusky or ashy markings, it is the European. If the underwing is pale gray and not mottled, it is the baldpate, or American widgeon.

Both are a medium-sized duck with a purplish-pink body, white breast and black hindquarters. The head is of a white-brown hue with a green patch on the face running through the eye. They appear at a distance as small brownish ducks and sit buoyantly on the water, chest low and tail well elevated. The bend of the wing is carried low and the wing tips are pointed upwards. They pivot frequently as they feed and appear ever on the alert even when hungry. The shiny white crown of the male's head gives the slight piebald appearance, hence the name baldpate.

These are swift flying ducks and are usually seen in compact flocks in irregular formation. Led by the master, they wheel and whiffle in a jerky zig-zag flight even though they are not frightened. When on the water they take alarm quickly and bounce into the air almost vertically and seem to spin quickly out of range.

The American variety breeds exclusively in northeastern North America. Large numbers of the species spend their winters on this continent though some seem to prefer the West Indies and parts of Central and South America.

I can recall spending a winter on the Yucatan Peninsula and having widgeon and teal regularly on the menu at the local hotels in Merida and Progresso. Market hunting below the border is still rampant and thousands of these ducks are killed each year despite international treaties, rules and regulations. It is amazing how much of our waterfowl are killed by the thousands as staple food down there, while we not only limit ourselves in our hunting, but spend large sums of money to develop the duck flocks and improve their breeding grounds in Canada and the North.

Normally, the widgeon feeds in the daylight hours on a mixed diet of vegetable and animal food, combining weeds, grasses, cockles and roots. The flock is often guided by an alert leader who directs them to a pond or marsh to surface feed and "tip" for food. The variance of their diet is responsible for the difference in their taste at the table. I have savored many a widgeon that was as good as teal and mallard when taken while feeding in fresh water. However, the same species that has been taken from the brackish marshes has a far different flavor.

The female lays from seven to ten eggs of whitish-cream color, the eggs of the two species being almost identical.

When you have the opportunity to watch these birds feed and play at ease, you'll have quite a show. During the winter months, particularly after the duck season is over, they relax their nervousness a trifle. Watching them in company with other shore birds along such areas as the St. John's River in Florida is quite an experience. I have often come upon them while bass fishing or trolling for shad. They are fairly easy to approach in the closed season and will decoy readily during the southward migration in the fall. Few ducks will decoy on their northern migration for they do not have a tendency to flock.

Study the migration maps published by the government. You'll also find such maps available from the conservation departments of the states. They have also been published in many bird books. From them you will be able to determine at what time of the year certain species can be seen in your immediate neighborhood.

The **blue-winged, green-winged** and **cinnamon teal** can be grouped together because of the similarity of their habits and characteristics.

They are all fast fliers, good to eat, beautifully marked birds, fairly easy to identify even in bad light. Called the midgets of the webfoot world, they are the smallest of the ducks and travel farther north and south than most of their relatives. They are hardy ducks, nesting over a wide area from northern Alaska to the Dakotas and Nebraska. When the frosty weather comes they scatter across the country from California and Mexico to the Carolinas. The European or greenwing teal nests in the Aleutian Islands clear to Greenland. The slightly larger bluewing does not go as far north or south. All species can be found in varying degrees from the Carolinas clear across Florida and the Gulf Coast during the winter months, with the bulk of the species wintering in Mexico, Panama, Caribbean Islands and several countries in South America.

How fast do teal fly? Ask any gunner and he will tell you that the teal is the fastest flier of the game, but the scientist disagrees, stating that the duck hunter is under the stress of optical illusion, and that due to the bird's small size it appears to be flying faster than, say, a mallard that is going full speed. This

50

probably accounts for so many missed birds. Their flight is seldom straight and true, but is broken constantly by dipping and swerving, making them a difficult target to follow and lead properly for a clean shot.

Many duck hunters will pass up the bigger species and wait for the teal to come over the blind, for here is the sportiest of birds and also, in the minds of many, far superior in taste to most others. Fly tiers use many of the teal's feathers in their art.

The young sportsman wishing to adorn his den with well-mounted specimens should certainly include a brace of flying teal, greenwings, especially. Their beautifully marked heads and wing decorations are examples of Mother Nature's finest art work. Miniature teal decoys carved out of wood and authentically hand painted also make fine decorations and you don't have to kill a bird to make one.

The green-winged teal is quickly recognizable by its head markings. The rust-red, semi-crested head is graced by a velvet green strip beginning at the eye and extending to the back of the lower part of the crest. There is a dash of white in the form of a half-moon at the shoulder, noticeable particularly when the duck is standing at rest with wings folded in. The wings are generally grey-brown, but the iridescent panel markings are green, fronted by a definitely marked pink stripe.

The blue-winged teal has a longer bill, and smaller grey-blue head that is not crested. A half-moon white marking comes between the eye and the bill. The large light blue first section of the wing is followed by a white band and then a rich green section of feathers, making it quite impossible to mistake it for any other species.

The cinnamon teal is cinnamon-colored all over except that the wing is just about the same as the blue-winged teal.

All three attract well to properly placed decoys, not necessarily representing them. Black duck or mallard decoys will often suffice. Since these are very wary birds, it is best to have a very concealing blind for the hunter or photographer in order to have enough time before they discover you. They are fun to watch when they begin to feed, for they constantly talk to each other in an incessant gabble, tipping up their tails to the sky as they head under for bits of plant life.

Their numbers vary in many locations from year to year, but they seem to survive the depredations of civilization. In recent years, their numbers have held up much better than others, particularly the readhead, a species often found with them when they are in wide open areas such as sounds, bays and inland waterways.

You are fortunate if you live in the area east of the Mississippi, for you will be able to find the **woodduck.** There are also a few in southern British Columbia, Washington and Oregon with strays in northern California.

Their numbers are solid from Virginia to northern Maine.

This is by far the most beautiful of the game bird ducks of America. The hooded merganser, technically not a game bird, but a beautiful duck, is about his only rival. "Woodie" has been hunted for sport, meat and for plumage, and, as a result, took a terrible beating from market hunters until laws protected him. The first Swamp Act of 1849 started the drainage of about 70 million acres of water and marsh lands, its natural habitat, and this did additional damage, for it killed off his chance to live and breed in those sections of the country. In 1918 legislation in Canada saved the bird from extinction. The woodduck is still not on the hunting list in many states. Where it is legal game, only one bird per season is allowed. The feathers are used by fly tiers in making trout flies.

Many breeders of exotic birds for estates and parks kept the strain alive and stocking was responsible for bringing back the species in areas where it had been lost seemingly forever.

While the bird is extremely shy, it will nest readily in tree

53

boxes placed alongside lakes and ponds or in marshes and swamps. The bird normally nests in trees, rather than on the ground, as the other ducks do.

The male is our only surface feeder with a crest on its head. Woodies are small, averaging eighteen inches long and weigh only one and a half pounds. They sit high on the water and their flight is swift and direct. Their food consists of aquatic plants, seeds and nuts.

Very seldom will you find a sizable flight of these birds, as they usually are prone to remain individuals, living in solitude in the marshes and protected lake shores. Usually, you will come upon them on some lost lake way back in the wilderness while on a camping or fishing trip. You might see one or two families at a time. They do not migrate to any great extent, often staying in one area and in one spot if conditions warrant. They are hardy and can usually ride out the winter. They do not require water all the time and so can get along during the freeze-ups.

If you reside west of the Great Lakes and in the northern states across to Oregon or north to Alaska, along the lower East and West Coasts or down into Mexico, you stand a good chance to see the **pintail,** one of the prettiest flying ducks of the entire list.

The pintail is a duck that wanted to be a goose. He has a long neck, longer than any other duck, and lets you know it in flight and when feeding on land or in the water. He also sports a pin tail, usually made of two or three sharp tail feathers, which extend a few inches beyond the ring of tail feathers. He is a medium-sized alert-looking duck with a bronze-brown head, white neck and breast with brownish-rust wings. Because of the long neck and the spiked tail he cannot possibly be mistaken for any other duck.

"Sprigs," as they are called, are fast erratic fliers, working the winds in irregular bunchy flights that seem to keep no air form, but vary constantly as they twist and turn, often without any apparent reason. Exceedingly shy, they will circle a pond several times before coming in. At just about the time you have your camera or gun set for action, something will scare them and they will instantly fly almost straight up and away.

They are quite often found in company with mallards, teal and other pond ducks and they will decoy readily to either black or mallard "blocks."

Pintails seem to be in good supply. They migrate very early in the spring, almost before one would think it was time to see any bird coming north. They are also an early breeder, laying as many as ten eggs at a time.

One of the prettiest set of pictures can be had when they are tipping up, feeding underwater. Their tails dance in the sunlight. Then, when they come up, and swallow their food they will literally stand on the water, fan their wings, stick out their neck as if to stretch it a bit for further feeding. That kind of photo sequence added to a good picture of their flight across the sunset sky will add a great thrill to your album. They do not breed in the Arctic, but many a nest is come upon in the resort areas of our northern states and in Canada.

The **gadwall** is a world traveler, and is found in all but South America and Australia. One of the most prolific birds, it offers great opportunities for the naturalist. Despite much encroachment of civilization, the gadwall stands up in defiance to it all.

Our western and central regions get the heaviest flights of these birds. The author has seen clouds of them during their wintering sessions in Florida. They are later migrants in the spring than most other ducks, preferring to make sure that the ice is out. They nest later, quite often into early summer. I have come upon their nests while fishing in the northern states. They hit the air trail sooner than the rest when the first signs of fall appear.

On the water they appear as a medium-sized duck, of general greyish-brown hue, and can be confused in bad light with the blackduck. Their wings sport irregular patches of cinnamon, black and off-white, but other than that they are rather drab in appearance. They make up for this by their cocky attitude and constant nervous activity while on the water.

They decoy more easily than most other ducks and do not become frightened quite as fast as blacks, teal or pintails. They are the amateur hunter's duck, for they are not particularly fast fliers.

Foodwise, they are similar to the blackduck, though not quite so tasty.

Most hunters pass them up, due to the low bag limits, preferring to let them come into the blind and the decoys with the hope that other species, seeing them, will be attracted.

Since they are so available they make great practice birds for your experience in action and long distance telephoto photography.

Chapter V

Diving Ducks

Unfortunately, the **redhead,** one of our grandest and once one of our most common game birds is in a serious downward cycle of abundance. He has been removed from the list of shootable waterfowl, and not completely due to hunting pressure. Despite the sportsmen's hard fight and cooperation from government and private agencies, the redhead's nesting areas, due to drainage and lack of water, are in bad shape.

These areas are in North and South Dakota, Utah and to some extent in southern Oregon, northern California, and particularly in the neighboring provinces of Canada. It is true that all duck species depend on the good nesting season in order to produce sufficient ducks to maintain the line. When these areas are troubled, the birds suffer. The redhead is a case in point. Cutting out the shooting of this species will never help much to bring it back, but, in times of great stress birds have to be protected by any and all means.

The only other duck that could possibly be mistaken for the redhead is the canvasback, although even a glimpse of the two birds would spell the difference. The little redhead has a round cinnamon-colored head, the canvasback's is larger and slanted into the long heavy bill.

They and the birds that follow in this chapter are classed as diving ducks, as opposed to puddle ducks of the previous chapter. Their feet are placed farther back on their bodies so that they can swim under water to get their food. As a consequence, they cannot bounce from the water as readily as, say, the mallard, but beat their wings and work their legs in the forward take-off, in order to get into the air. As divers, they have a great deal more and varied food available to them.

Their wintering grounds are found along the East Coast from Delaware to Georgia, but the bulk of the migration centers west of the Mississippi on the Gulf Coast. They travel in V-shaped formations, though irregular bunchy flights often swing in behind the conventional wedge.

They are a prolific duck and when conditions allow, there would be no need to worry, as they lay up to ten or fifteen eggs, and sometimes two clutches a year, if conditions favor.

Although the **old squaw** is a duck of extremely small range, it is covered here because it is such a "cute" bird, one which, if you are lucky enough to see and photograph will offer many inspiring memories.

Their wintering grounds extend from South Carolina north to Maine, New Brunswick and Nova Scotia, breeding and summering in the very far north including the northern shores of Greenland and Iceland.

They are a small, brown and white duck with a cocky little semi-crested head and a pin tail that is haughtily waved in an almost upright position when they swim. They are a fast flying bird, working the shore in compact flocks, whizzing and buzzing the shoreline in almost snipe-like fashion.

They like the open waters as well as the bays and inland waterways. Quite often, while in search of food, they will swim the waves in a long irregular line, until some one of the group finds food. At the signal, they descend one by one to feed, but always keep a certain amount of their numbers on the water to sight danger.

They are not a good duck for the table, their food being almost ninety percent of animal origin. That, combined with their salt water haunt, makes them a duck to see, appreciate and enjoy rather than to shoot, unless a specimen is wanted for mounting purposes. Many states have this bird off the hunting list, so, as in all cases, each season, check with the game laws.

The sighting of these ducks will be a pleasant accident. You might be out coot shooting or possibly a few might come by when you are out after canvasbacks. Conservation can do little for them, as their nesting areas are beyond control of man and their southward migration is so limited.

Three ducks which are the most difficult of all to tell apart are the **ring-necked duck** and the great and lesser scaup. Even experts will argue when they have the actual specimens in hand. Usually a bird book with accurate identifications is consulted.

The ring-necked duck has a black tip, a white band and a grey band on the bill. The others have light blue-grey bills as will be detailed later.

The winter plumage of the adult male consists of a black head and neck, glossed with purple iridescence, sometimes glowing a green or reddish-green sheen.

The head is marked by a crown, where the others are round headed. The breast is a shiny black without the iridescence and the belly is white. The wings are an indistinct brown-grey. The female does not wear the crest but carries the band of white on the bill. She is mostly mottled-brown in general appearance.

Their wintering grounds extend from the tip of Florida to the Carolinas and westward to the Mississippi, the greatest concentration settling along the Gulf Coast. During the summer months, you can readily find them nesting in upper New England, New Brunswick and Nova Scotia. They seldom go farther north except in the midwest fly-way where they go up beyond and west of Hudson's Bay. There is a small amount of them on the West Coast along the shores of British Columbia and down into the San Francisco Bay area of California.

The ringneck is a first-class table bird, although its smaller size causes the hunter to pass it up for the larger and more popular species. It is preferred over the scaup and golden eye. The species decoy readily and generally pitch right in without fanfare or a pre-scanning trip. Many will come bulleting in at once, their little feet and fast wings momentarily set to break the flight and the water when they splash in. They are quite a sight as they hit the water. If you are lucky enough go get this picture, it will be one that will bring laughs. The ducks seem to be very clumsy

at that point, especially if you are able to stop them cold in mid-flight. They flock in open formation and sometimes come into the blind in a string or all at once in a bunch like grapes.

They are essentially a freshwater duck although they do find their way to the wetlands of the coastal areas where brackish waters are present. Almost all of their food is made up of vegetation and they dive for shoots the puddle ducks cannot reach.

They are particularly nervous while feeding, floating or walking about clumsily on the ground. Why the nervousness does not apply to the times they come into the decoys we do not know, but it is fortunate for the hunter that they are so easy to attract.

They normally nest in wet, boggy places along the edges of marshes, sloughs and ponds. The actual nest is barely above the level of the water and it would seem that the eggs would be subject to wetting if the level of the water should rise from a sudden rainfall. The female lays from eight to twelve eggs. As is usual with all ducks, the mother assumes all the duties, the males having long since departed to spend the summer as bachelors, until the time of the autumn flight when they rejoin the females for the trip south.

Their fall migration starts in October and in the spring they work northward slowly, starting in April, if the weather permits. They are quite often seen in the north just as the ice goes out from the lakes.

Telling the **greater scaup** and the **lesser scaup** apart is quite a chore for the accurate bird watcher and naturalist. Few duck hunters can tell them apart in flight or on the water unless they know the markings well and the light is exceptionally good.

The difference between the greater and lesser scaup is in the markings of the wings. The white band of color along the wings continues into the tip flight feathers on the greater scaup, but does not go beyond the bend of the wing in the lesser.

Other than this, they are identical in markings, both having light blue-grey bills. The female of both types has a white band between the bill and the eye, but this is not found on either of the males. The female of the ringneck has a narrow white band on the base of the bill but not in the feathers. The flight feathers on the ringneck do not have any white. Sitting on the water together it would be quite difficult to tell them apart.

The greater scaup winters along the West Coast as far south as central California and summers in northwest Canada and most of Alaska. The lesser scaup covers this area, plus the Eastern Seaboard from New England south to the West Indies, and Mexico.

Scaups fly in a rapid pace, in compact formation, without the form of a V and seldom in long strings. When they fly by the blind in full speed the noise from their wings sounds like a hurricane wind whistling through the trees. They often fly at great height during the migration, coming down at dusk or just after nightfall, thus avoiding the gunners.

They are both favorites of the hunter because of their numbers. The best way to attract them is with decoys of their coloration. Large rafts of decoys are used rather than just a few, as in the case of the puddle ducks.

Their food is one-half vegetable and one-half animal, so their diet is not a restricting factor in their choice of location for breeding purposes.

Periodically, slight variances in their number occur, but it is supposed that they are in no great danger of reaching dangerously low levels.

F.W.D.

The **goldeneye** is widely and aptly called the "whistler" or "whistlewing," due to the high pitched, vibrant swishing sounds made by its wings during flight. It is widely distributed across our land and into Canada, being scarce in the Southwest. Its nearest relative is the Barrow's goldeneye, a bird with very similar markings.

The goldeneye sports a shiny blue-green head, supported by a white neck and breast. The "eye" is a white circular spot located below the eye and just behind the bill. Small as it is, it is readily seen from quite a distance even in bad light. The similar mark on the Barrow's is more triangular in shape. Both species have a broad patch of white against the black-brown on the wing. The two species are found in the Northeast and Northwest, the Barrow's being limited exclusively to these areas.

In flight they can be seen for a great distance as a black and white bird whisking along at great speed. They are a hardy duck migrating north to the lakes of Maine, where the author has seen them while salmon fishing, the moment the ice has left the lakes.

Small bands of them will fly past the boat, travelling up and down the linking streams between the lakes. They are a friendly duck and are easily decoyed into a blind.

Watching them while at play is a humorous experience, for they seem to enjoy life to the fullest, dabbling, tipping up, diving, fanning their wings and chattering incessantly.

They prefer a lake that is surrounded by trees, for they, like the woodchuck, seem to prefer to nest just off the ground, preferably in a dead stump. They have been known to start building a nest in a boat tied along the shore.

Goldens are not of the best eating variety, feeding on bugs, crustaceans, including crabs, snails, mollusks and fishes.

When migrating they fly in small flocks or in a bunch. They like the high altitudes and make a pretty sight flashing black and white way up there in the blue.

F.W.Davis

Since the food of the **bufflehead duck** is almost all animal, it is not sought after by hunters to the same degree as most other ducks. It is a beautiful little bird, presenting flashes of black and white in flight and on the water. Smaller than most ducks yet larger than the teal, they are seen in broken flocks, usually not too high above the water. Like the old squaws, they feed in platoons, always reserving a few ducks above the water for danger lookouts. They seem to be able to alternate feeders and watchers in quite a regulated rhythm.

The main identifying feature of the bufflehead is the large white patch on the head, readily distinguishable from the little spot worn by the goldeneye. The head is semi-crested. The neck and breast are white, the wings black, except for a small section of white.

They become quite frightened when approached and are very active when feeding or playing. They constantly duck, fan their wings and take off in small flights over the water, to return again to the same spot. Their flight in singles or pairs is quite direct unless they sense danger. They can take off from the water with surprising ease, since they are of the diving duck variety, which usually has to fight gravity during the forward take-off. They ride high on the water and are perky, quick moving and lively.

When they dive they are as adept as the grebes and mergansers, holding the wings in close to the body. They can stay underwater quite a time, and swim away from danger quickly that way.

They belong to the small group of tree-nesting ducks and their eggs are laid in abandoned flicker nests and other tree holes. Only when forced by circumstance will they nest on the ground, and even then will try and build in a bush if there is one handy.

Their distribution is wide, the only blank in the map being the central Midwest. They nest as far north as southern Alaska and down into Ontario and west to the Pacific. Their southern home overlaps in Oregon and Washington and they are found as far south as the Mexican border and the Gulf States, skipping Florida for the most part.

Their migration takes place in the middle of the fall and they fly north just as soon as the ice is gone in the northern lakes. Their habits are similar to the goldeneye.

To the hunter, the mere mention of the **canvasback duck** conjures up the sight of rafts of a hundred decoys, grouped around a sink box or skillfully camouflaged duck boat, in open water, with cold, windy, dreary weather and flights of canvasbacks streaking across the sky.

Colored and shaped somewhat like the redhead, except for the larger shape that is angular instead of round, the canvasback sports a big heavy bill. Their tails are black. The basic body and wings are canvas-grey in color. The breast is black and the head and neck the typical amber-cinnamon. Seen together, they are readily distinguishable from the smaller redhead.

It is exclusively a North American species and is not found even as a straggler in any other country. Its numbers and availability have made it famous among duck hunters on both coasts, the heaviest concentration being on the East Coast from New England south across Georgia, skipping Florida and along the Gulf Coast down into Mexico. The West Coast has a lesser flight that extends up into British Columbia. They nest from Utah and Nebraska up into the prairie provinces of Western Canada using all three flyways for their migrations north and south. The Great Lakes region gets a late migration in the fall and much hunting is done for them in that section.

One of the best ways to obtain photos of these ducks is to accompany a duck hunter in his duck boat and wait for the flocks to fly overhead. Quite often a smart hunter will allow the first flock to "sit in" with the blocks in order to attract a larger flock. When they light, they look over the blocks and then disregard them entirely, not being perturbed that they are fakes. Unless something scares them, they will stay for a while, and at a given signal from one of the leaders will all take flight at the same instant.

They have maintained their numbers, despite bad conditions in the nesting grounds due to low or non-existent water. They have fared much better than the redhead duck, which is now off the shooting list, yet the canvasback nests in the same general areas.

Their numbers have diminished in the past few years, as have almost all the ducks, but seem to indicate no trouble in the near future.

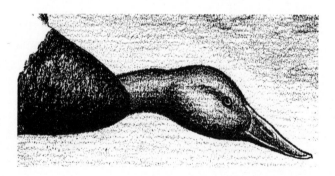

The **shoveller duck** is not too common and is protected in most states from hunting. At first sight, way off from the blind, his green head makes you think he is a mallard, but as he comes closer his wing beats and size show him to be what he is. A closer look shows the tremendous beak, almost twice the size of the mallard's. His breast is white, rather than russet, as the mallard. His flanks are a reddish-cinnamon. His wings are colored somewhat like the greenwing teal, with the large light-blue patch on the first section of the wing.

The female is colored about like the female mallard, and the only way to distinguish them is by the long bill worn by the shoveller.

They are sporadic on the East Coast, their biggest flyway being the West Coast and inland to Utah from British Columbia to central Mexico.

The common name **"coot,"** has been used here, as duck hunters and amateur bird spotters give this name to three species of scoters.

The white-winged scoter, surf scoter and American scoter are birds of one distinct class with special habits. They are sometimes found intermingled in the same flock and duck hunters have difficulty identifying one or the other as they approach the blind.

While some people eat coot, their meat is about the worst tasting of all the ducks. I have hunted them with friends who were excited about the sport. I went along just to see the fun but, frankly, couldn't find it. Certainly, after the first bite, I passed up the coot dinner.

All three species are found on both coasts from eastern Canada to Virginia, and from British Columbia to California. They are tough birds resisting the foul weather of the north until it practically forces them southward. Their flight is usually just above the waves. They come into the blind head-on and look as if they were going to crash into your duck boat. Their speed is fast and their flight direct.

The American scoter is black all over except for a bright orange "bubble" at the top of the bill. The female is dark brown. The white-winged scoter is marked about the same, but with a small patch of white on the first section of the wing. The surf scoter is all dingy black, but with a patch of white on the back of the head and upper neck, and another white patch on the "cap" of the head. The bill is orange and white, with a decided black circular spot at its base. The legs of the others are black, but the surf scoter's are a dull orange.

The whitewing is the largest and probably the most common of the trio and the one most coveted by hunters. Their flight is direct, heavy and dull. They usually travel in bunches, but alternate from bunched-up gatherings to long single lines.

They are slow taking off from the water, usually needing a good headwind and lots of runway space that is smooth for the take-off. Watching them try to take off in a rough sea is quite an experience, for the waves will slap at them just as they are about to become free.

Chapter VI

Geese

From a distance the **Canada goose** is easily identified. His body is brown, neck and head black, but his head wears a triangular white patch. He is the biggest of our geese, and is found either as a resident or a migrator over most of the United States.

In the spring and fall, he is seen flying very high in great long wedges to and from his wintering and summer breeding grounds, coming down into city parks, reservations and sanctuaries for a rest period and for food.

Their voices are strong as they are heard uttering a loud resonant "honk" in flight or on the water. While feeding, or together on a pond, they talk in little intimate cries and grunts.

This is the hunter's bird, being the most sought after of the geese. As a result "Canada" has become exceedingly wary, putting down only after having scanned and circled the area with much care. Their sharp eyes can quickly spot a hunter and the best of blinds can be discovered. Second only to the wild swans, the Canada is a big bird on the dinner table, weighing from seven to fourteen pounds, with a wing spread of between five and 6½ feet.

Contrary to the ducks, which seek new mates each season, the Canada goose is supposed to mate for life. Should either partner die or be killed, it is said that the mate never "remarries." Just why Mother Nature chose to make this arrangement, no one knows, but she must have had her reasons. Certainly this is a drawback to the numbers of the Canada. A certain amount of good can be done by raising these gallant game birds and stocking areas with them, and in fact this is being done in many sections of the country. The biggest cause of death to these birds is not the hunter, but pollution of the waters in which it lands along its flight routes. Development of wetlands and shore property have lessened the areas of comparative remoteness where "Honkers" will consider landing. They simply will not come down where there are signs of civilization, unless it is a sanctuary. They can spot such a safe spot by looking over the other birds on the water and will feel safe in landing.

Jack Minor of Kingston, Ontario, was the first to recognize the need for sanctuaries for this grand game bird. Starting with the small pond on his property, he fed the geese during the migration seasons until tremendous flights of them would return to his care each year. The sanctuary has grown in size and has been financed, for the feeding bill for these birds is enormous. Others have followed in his footsteps, so that the Canada is assured at least a few spots where it is safe. Banding has helped to discover their migrations.

This goose generally nests on the ground near the water. The type of nest depends on the locality. It is usually a slight depression in the ground lined with material from the vicinity such as sticks, flag grass and soft grey down from the goose's breast. At other times the nests are large bulky affairs. In some parts of the country when the terrain demands, the nests are in trees, but never far from the water and preferably right above it.

During the breeding season the gander, or male goose shows off his staunchness as the family guard and defender. If you approach the nest they will at first look at you with contempt. Come closer and they will become alarmed and hiss, wave their powerful wings and be ready to pick a fight. The author has had many a battle with them without so much as provoking one, so true to their cause do they become when an intruder comes by. Don't underestimate their powerful wings; they can knock you down very easily and, even though they have no teeth in their bills, they are sharp, and if they bite you, the cut can be quite severe.

Unlike the ducks, both parents are quite taken up with caring for the young. When swimming on the water, the gander usually leads, the little ones follow and then mother takes up the tail of the parade.

Their food is largely vegetable matter. They love to graze in the stubble fields and the prairies. Pasture lands are their pleasure, particularly during the fall migration, for they burn up a great deal of energy during the flight, which must be replaced. Quite often, clouds of them will descend on a farmer's corn field, even though there is little or no water nearby. They have been known to be quite destructive in this habit.

The Canada is one of the earliest water birds to migrate northward in the spring. How it is they know that the ice is melted from the lakes, when they are wintering one or two thousand miles south, is a mystery, but they know it and proceed.

After the summer molt they become quite inactive. Then they begin to gain back their flight feathers, begin to assemble in flocks and become restless. On a cool night when the winds are right, they will take off on the first leg of a long journey, husbands and wives flying together. They are masters at knowing flight patterns and wind resistance. Their flying wedge is so designed that the lead goose breaks the currents for the rest of the wedge. After a spell, the lead goose drops back to the end of the line and the succession continues so that no bird takes the brunt of the wind.

While very rare on the East Coast and the eastern half of the continent, the **white-fronted goose** are comparatively abundant throughout the West. The breeding range is in the polar regions all the way around, so they are also found in Europe and Asia. In our land they are known as the "laughing geese," due to their peculiar laugh-cry sound, as it is heard while they are in flight as well as on the ground or water. In Europe they winter around the Mediterranean and, in our hemisphere, in and around the Gulf and the southern states.

Like the Canada geese, they seem to time their arrival in the north to just when the ice is out and the farmer's fields are beginning to grow tender shoots of grain and corn. They also feed on heath berries. Their mating season is generally over by the end of May and a nest filled with as many as five to seven eggs will be laid. The male does not desert the female in the family processes, but stands by at all times to do his duty. These geese are difficult to conserve, because the northern people go after them for food, especially when they are molting and cannot fly.

Some unseen and unknown force sets the white-fronted geese off for the southward migration long before many of the other waterfowl. Great flights of them will be coming down in California well in advance of the rest. Their flight is a modified V and sometimes great flocks of them will assemble behind the flying wedge that is breaking the wind force. They fly quite high to avoid the ground currents and also the hunters.

It is not definitely known whether they, like the Canada geese, mate for life, though there seems to be much evidence in the favor of the belief, for it seems to be a common characteristic of geese.

They are an easy bird to identify on the ground or in flight. Their head and entire neck is brownish grey with a white band around the front of the face. Their body is greyish brown. The belly and flanks are white speckled with irregular dark brown splotches.

As is the case with all migratory waterfowl, they are protected by federal regulations as to hunting. The states adapt these dates to their situation along with bag limits. They are quite easy to bring down to a set of decoys. When the day comes and you have your camera ready, a flight of these birds zooming in on powerful wings against a crisp blue sky backed by the haze of far-off mountains will make a picture you will treasure.

There are several other geese that are somewhat similar in size, coloring and habits such as the emperor, found mostly in Alaska, the tule goose, found mainly in California, the lesser snow goose, of the Great Lakes region and the greater snow goose found along the Middle Atlantic states. The whitefront was selected for our study because of its extreme popularity and the fact that it is representative of the group.

The **American brant** and its close cousin, the **black brant,** are a sort of half-way measure in size between the largest of the geese and the usual ducks. They appear on the water as very small dark geese with short blackish necks and whitish sides. They sit very lightly on the water with tail upraised and the flight half of the wings pointed upwards, somewhat in the fashion of the teal ducks.

Brant are also called the white-bellied brant. They are a true sea goose, seldom found very far away from the salt water. They are rarely found on the Pacific Coast, and the American's flight pattern is from Labrador to Florida and into the West Indies, though seldom moving farther south in the mass than the Carolinas.

The black is strictly a West Coast migrant, seldom if ever being found East of the California mountains.

American brant nest in the Far North and are found in company with eider ducks. The nest is of local materials such as mosses and lichens, with a plentiful lining of breast down feathers to ward off the northern cool breezes found there even in the summer.

The number of eggs varies from three to eight. As soon as the young can stand on their webbed feet they are drawn to the salt water as if by a magnet, the mothers and fathers aiding them to do so. At once they begin to feed and fend for themselves.

Brant do not usually fly in V-shape flocks but bunch together. Their trip is not as far as the Canada, and they do not generally fly as high.

At the table the brant, in the opinion of epicures, is one of our finest game birds, despite the fact that they feed and live in the salt water. Their northern feed consists of grass, algae, moss and stalks and leaves of arctic plants. Farther south they tend to feed on grass shoots, roots and other vegetation.

They generally start the southward migration along the East Coast in early September but head back again from their Carolina sites as early as March.

Flights of these birds can be seen in the sanctuaries along the East Coast in spring and fall. They are not hunted to any great degree, except in a few isolated places. While not a dramatically marked bird, they do make good camera subjects. They should certainly be among the birds seen and identified on your bird list.

If you live in the path of the **blue goose,** it will be no trouble to find during the migrating and nesting season, for it winters on the coast of Louisiana, and covers the territory of the general Mississippi valley, flying as far north as Manitoba and James Bay.

On the water it appears as a medium-sized goose, readily identifiable by its white neck and head and dark body. In flight they are even easier to identify because of the great color contrast. They fly in modified V's and bunches. Their call, particularly in the air, is a high-pitched whistle and chatter of high notes.

This is one goose which has increased in numbers during the past few years. Their habits are similar to the other geese mentioned in this book.

A good way to find the best times to see these and other migratory waterfowl is to study the game laws and discover the open hunting areas, as well as the sanctuaries. You can go there with your camera and glasses and see this grand game bird. There is a certain majesty about geese that no other game bird seems to display. Watching them descend on the water, or take off, bunch together and assemble a flight pattern is something to observe. Here you will witness true organization at its best.

CHAPTER VII

Game Birds, Your Heritage and Responsibility

The study of American game birds is actually the study of the country itself, from the standpoint of nature and outdoor life. Where proper conditions for these species exist, you will find them in varying numbers according to the amount of disturbance man has caused in their environment, feeding and isolation.

There remain areas in the country which support many of the species mentioned in this book, where man's destructive effect is hardly noticed at all. In other places, the wild game has been forced by real estate development, wetlands drainage, commercialization, roads and pollution, to retire into more remote areas. Man has further unbalanced this remaining land and water by allowing natural and domestic predators, such as the house cat and dog, to run wild and feed on game.

However, there are signs, just beginning to be seen, that the country has finally awakened to the need to support the wild things and to guarantee their future needs. State conservation agencies, together with various departments of the federal government, have combined with owners of large tracts of land, such as the lumber and pulp companies, to bring about a multiple-use program—harvesting the timber and crops along with protection for the wilds, for man's and the creatures' benefit. It is here that organizations such as the Izaak Walton League Of America, the Audubon Society and others have helped in great measure.

In still more areas of the country, the practices of conservation have enabled man to repair the damage he has done to the wilds, and to restock the fields and forests with many species for the nature lover as well as the sportsman.

Throughout all this development, it has been the sportsman who initially has been the most active of any group to guard against the bleak future of disappearing wildlife and to see that strong measures must be undertaken. Finally his voice has been heard. Many states are going on land-buying programs to set aside lands for wild-life sanctuaries, recreational parks and forests. Game bird species will thrive in these areas, particularly the birds like the grouse and the snipe, neither of which is given to artificial propagation as are the pheasant and the ducks.

That these steps forward will be maintained and increased in intensity is entirely up to you—the next generation. Those who have gone before, preaching, campaigning and actually fighting for the rights of the outdoors and the wild things, must eventually turn over the reins of government and sporting interests to the next electorate who will take over, as is their right.

This is a big package, loaded with many responsibilities. Industry and an expanding population is land-hungry, and the lessons of pillaging the natural resources have not yet been sufficiently learned by enough people to cause their designs to include conservation in any and all of its interlocking facets.

It will be an easy task to see just how well you are doing. Where the wild creatures cannot live any longer, you will not find them. This is the danger signal, for when they and their example of balanced nature leave, the human family is doomed to depart sooner or later. Where water becomes scarce and unreliable, life cannot prosper. Where soil has been eroded or drained of its values, proper food cannot grow and man, along with his wild charges, must eventually depart.

There are many who falsely criticize the sportsman and single him out as the one who has hunted the wild creatures to death. They claim that if we did not have hunters, there would be more wild creatures in the woods, fields and swamps. This is simply not so. The sportsman does take a small harvest annually of the game bird population in areas where it is legal. But remember, that it is the sportsman who has been the one to pay for the game protector and warden, the scientific laboratory and mechanics of the state conservation departments through license fees, and sporting goods taxes. The sportsman has created and supported such efforts as Ducks Unlimited, without which we would probably have few if any ducks flying at all. Do some research on this organization, as an example, and you will see that the sportsman's organizations have actually put money, brains and efforts into the protection of the wilds. Many other organizations have merely talked about it, or instituted sanctuaries, largely because the owners of the property have given it over to the cause merely to dodge taxes.

The way you can help as an individual is to join a rod and gun club and see to it that conservation is the number one subject at the meetings and that more than just debate goes on. All these clubs are aligned under regional or county federations and thus form a network of power which is felt by the state and federal politicians. Surveys have shown that there are a tremendous amount of people who hunt and fish, and who, also, vote.

Investigate the 4-H Clubs which also contribute much effort and practical assistance on their important grass roots level.

There are those who are against the killing of birds and animals. Being against this, however, is not going to guarantee wildlife safety against infringing civilization. The man who shoots a few pheasants or grouse or ducks can do more for wildlife in general, because of his interest and contact, for he is not only interested solely in killing game. Being a sportsman, he realizes that the sports of hunting and fishing are basic training for sportsmanship and honesty in dealing with life itself. Few youngsters who have been exposed to the sports have been juvenile delinquents. The two just don't mix. Furthermore, just because someone does not shoot a bird or an animal does not make him a saint. By NOT doing something, "bad" you do not necessarily become "good." There are many people who do not go around murdering other people, but they are not necessarily good people!

Be proud of the fact that you like to hunt and bring home game. By the same token, do not lose your temper with those who call you a killer. They just don't understand.

As a sportsman, nature lover, and one who likes to see the wilds as they should be, you have a great responsibility, both to your fellow man and to the creatures of the wilds. Whether you like to catch a bird in the binoculars, on film in your camera, or whether, in addition, you like to dine on broiled grouse, you have the job of seeing to it that these creatures live as they should, despite encroaching civilization.

Some day you will hand over the reins to your own younger generation who will, in their turn, thank you for what you have done, and will want to keep what you have guarded for them.

Don't let them down!

Glossary

Barred Feathers which are marked with alternating light and dark bands.

Blind A constructed place covered and surrounded with natural grasses and branches in which the hunter hides in or near to see or shoot game.

Brace Two birds.

Clutch of Eggs The name given to a single laying of the usual amount at one nesting period.

Commercial Shooting Preserve A preserve privately owned that is stocked with birds or animals for the sole purpose of shooting them. A certain price is charged for each bird killed.

Covey A group of birds feeding or flying in a small tight group.

Decoy A wooden, plastic or rubber imitation of the real bird, used to attract the flying birds into the blind.

Flocking Birds that tend to fly together in a group.

Flushing Raising from their ground position to that of flying, by coming near with dog, or scared up from the ground by man.

Fowl A general term used to describe ducks and chickens.

Game Poachers Those people who shoot too many birds over the legal limit or shoot birds out of season or shoot on private property.

Gregarious The habit of living, feeding together in a group.

Haunts Favored locations for feeding, resting, nesting and living.

Hybrid A cross of bloodlines or species in breeding to produce a variant of the species.

Lead (Leed) The amount of sighting distance given by the gunner in order for the shot to intercept the bird in flight.

Leg Banding The placing of a metal or plastic band on the leg for later identification when bird is checked or shot. The purpose is to discover its flight pattern from area to area.

Migratory A bird that migrates, or travels in season from north to south or from south to north, or travels any regular pattern for food or nesting.

Naturalist One who studies nature and the living creatures.

Pinnated Feathers which are thin down at the tips to where the stem is almost bare of fibers.

Pointing Dog   The dog that points the game with its nose so the hunter can locate it.

Predators   Those animals or birds which feed on the flesh of other creatures.

Propogation   The breeding of animals and birds to produce young.

Ruffs   Feathered patches at the shoulder of the bird.

Sanctuary   That place designated by man to be set aside for the use of the birds. Protection is offered from hunting and molesting.

Species   The scientific name given to an established kind of animal or bird.

Stalk   To sneak up or approach without the animal knowing it.

Stocked   A bird or animal raised in captivity and released in the wild.

Bibliography

BETTEN, H. L. *Upland Game Shooting.* Philadelphia: Penn Publishing Co., 1940.

COLLINS, HENRY H. *Complete Guide to American Wildlife.* New York: Harper and Bros., 1959.

CONNETT, E. V. *Duck Shooting.* New York: William Morrow, 1947.

CRUICKSHANK, ALLAN D. *Pocket Guide to the Birds.* New York: Dodd, Mead, 1953.

EDMINSTER, FRANK C. *American Game Birds.* New York: Charles Scribner's 1954.

HEILNER, VAN CAMPEN. *A Book on Duck Shooting.* New York: Alfred Knopf, 1947.

HOLLAND, RAY P. *Shotgunning in the Lowlands.* West Hartford, Vt.: Countryman Press, 1945.

JORDAN, E. L. *Hammond's Nature Atlas of America.* Maplewood, N. J.: C. S. Hammond and Co., 1952.

LANE, FRANK W. *Nature Parade.* New York: Fawcett World Library, 1954.

PEARSON, T. GILBERT. *Birds of America.* New York: Garden City Books, 1936.

SHALDACH, WM. J. *Coverts and Casts.* New York: A. S. Barnes, 1943.

SPRUNT, ALEXANDER and ZIM, HERBERT S. *Game Birds.* New York: Golden Press, 1962.

STRINGFELLOW, ROBERT B. *Standard Book of Hunting and Shooting.* New York: Greystone Press, 1950.

Index

Africa, 26
Alaska, 41, 50, 66, 72
American wigeon (*see* Baldpate)
Arizona, 9
Asia, 26
Audubon Sanctuaries, 11, 32, 88

Baldpate, 47
Barnyard gobbler (*see* Wild Turkey)
Barrow's duck (*see* Goldeneye duck)
Binoculars, 11, 91
Bird watcher, 35
Birds of prey, 9
Birds, song, 9
Black Brant, 84
Black duck, 41, 42, 44
Blue Goose, 86
Blue-winged teal, 50
Boat, hunting, 38
Bobwhite quail, 21
Brant, 84
British Columbia, 53, 73, 75, 76
Buffle-head duck, 71

California, 9, 19, 23, 26, 29, 50, 53, 66, 76, 83
California Valley quail, 18
Canada, 16, 26, 28, 56, 66, 76
Canada goose, 79
Canvasback duck, 73
Central America, 41, 44, 48
Chicken, 14
Chinese pheasant (*see* Ringneck pheasant)
Christmas, 30
Clapper rail, 38

Climate, 9
Clubs, 4, 24, 91
Clutches, 29, 60
Cinnamon teal, 50
City parks, 40
Civilization, 15, 20, 30, 42, 52, 91
Commercial shooting preserve, 24, 40
Common snipe (*see* Jacksnipe)
Conservation, 14, 22, 23, 30, 32, 36, 42, 62, 87, 90
Coot, 76
Covey, 27

Decoy, 34, 41, 52, 58, 63, 66, 70, 83
Decoy miniature, 40
Delicacy, 27
Den, sportsman, 40, 42
Disease, 23, 28
Dog, bird, 11, 24, 25, 26, 32
Dog, pointer, 11, 19, 24
Dog, setter, 11, 15, 24
Dog, spaniel, 11
Droughts, 23
Duck, 37
Ducks Unlimited, 89

Eastern seaboard, 38
Europe, 26
European widgeon, 47
Extinction, 33

Federal regulations, 33, 42, 88
Fens, 9
Fires, 23
Flash gun, 37
Flocks, 17, 28, 34, 35, 36, 48, 71

Floods, 23
Florida, 21, 23, 30, 38, 49,
    57, 63, 72
Fowl, hunting, 25

Gadwall duck, 57
Gallinules, 38
Gambel's quail, 8, 18
Game birds, 9, 10, 32, 36, 87
Georgia, 21, 30
Gizzards, 14
Goldeneye duck, 69
Goose, Canada, 9
Greater Scaup, 66
Greenhead duck (*see* Mallard)
Greenland, 50, 61
Grouse, Franklin, 12
Grouse, ruffed, 9, 12, 15, 16, 36
Grouse, Hudsonian, 12
Grouse, sharp-tailed, 12, 16
Gun, 11, 26
Gunners, 17, 34

Habit, 10
Habitat, 10
Hackberry bush, 20
Heath hen, 16
Honkers (*see* Canada goose)
Hungarian Partridge, 26
Hunter, 17, 29, 35, 45, 66
Hunting, 11, 28, 32, 38, 39
Hybrid, 24

India, 26
Indians, 32
International treaties, 48

Jacksnipe, 33, 39
Jump shooting, 41

Labrador, 44
Lesser scaup, 66
Loggers, 12

Maine, 9, 36, 38, 53, 61, 69
Mallard duck, 40
Market hunting, 28, 48
Marsh, 9
Mating, 14, 19
Mexico, 28, 44, 50, 66, 73
Michigan, 21
Migrate, 9, 17, 28, 33, 35, 36,
    41, 49, 54, 70, 72, 82
Miner, Jack sanctuary, 80
Mississippi, 21
Mother Nature, 51, 79
Mourning dove, 28

Naturalist, 33, 57, 66
Nature, 12
Nature lovers, 11
Navajo country, 9
New England, 21
Newfoundland, 35, 41, 44
New Jersey, 21
New York, 21, 30, 36
New York City, 21
North America, 48
Northeast states, 12
North Carolina, 44, 50
Nova Scotia, 35, 36, 61

Old Squaw, duck, 60
Open season, 33
Oregon, 21, 23, 53, 72

Pacific states, 12
Parkways, 24
Pass shooting, 41
Pennsylvania, 44
Pheasant, English, 24
Pheasant, Mongolian, 24
Photographer, 9, 11, 17, 22,
    25, 34, 36, 37, 39, 43, 52,
    58, 74
Pidgeon, 28

Pintail duck, 41, 55
Plains states, 16, 26
Pollution, 36, 41, 79, 87
Prairie chicken, 9, 12, 16
Predators, 17, 19, 22, 41, 87
Puddle ducks, 40, 65

Real estate developers, 23, 36
Red head duck, 58
Red legs duck (*see* Black duck)
Restocking, 12, 19, 30, 42
Ring-neck duck, 63
Ringneck, 9, 23 (*see also*
    Pheasant)
Ruff, 9

Sage hen, 16
Sanctuary, 45
Seasons, 89
Shore birds, 33, 35
Shoveller duck, 75
South America, 50, 57
Species, 10, 14, 27, 41, 87
Sportsman, 9, 21, 27, 39, 51,
    89, 91
Sports Afield, Magazine, 11
Sprigs (*see* Pintail duck)
Stores, book, 11

Stores, sporting goods, 11
Surf scooter (*see* Coot)
Swale, 9
Swamp, 9

Teal, 41
Thanksgiving, 30
Timberdoodle (*see* Woodcock)
Trout fishermen, 37, 53

Virginia, 21

Waterfowl, 40
Washington, 23
West Indies, 48, 66
Whistler (*see* Goldeneye duck)
White fronted goose, 82
White winged dove, 28
White winged scooter
    (*see* Coot)
Widgeon, 41
Wild Life Sanctuary, 36
Wild turkey, 30
Woodduck, 58
Woodcook, 35

Yellow legs (*see* Mallard)
Yucatan peninsula, 48